Can I come in?

by Carol Matchett

Schofield & Sims

Jazz made a tent.

She went to get a pillow.

She went to get a box.

She went to get a torch.

"Can I come in?" said Ollie.

"No!" said Jazz.

Jazz went to get a sock.

She went to get some popcorn.

"Can I come in?" said Ollie.

"Yes," said Jazz.

"Come to my puppet show!"

Notes for parents and other helpers

Enjoying and talking about the story

CLL 1 responding to stories; **CLL 2** talking to develop ideas;
CLL 4 understanding of stories; **NLS** T9

- Remember that the most important thing is to have fun and enjoy the story!

- Make sure that you are both in the mood for a story before you begin.

- Read the title and discuss the cover, building a sense of anticipation: **'I wonder why this story is called "Can I come in?"'**

- When you read the story, point out that Ollie is intrigued by what Jazz is doing. Ask, **'What is happening in the tent?'**

- Encourage the child to think ahead and guess what might happen: for example (page 8), ask **'Why do you think Jazz needs a sock?'**, **'What is Ollie thinking?'**

- On page 11, encourage the child to predict why Jazz is now letting Ollie into tent and what he might find there. Then turn to page 12.

- Discuss the surprise ending (page 13): **'That's what Jazz was doing! She's made a *puppet theatre*!'** Point out items taken into the tent; observe how they have been used.

- Go back through the story, looking at the activities of the kittens – Salt and Pepper.

- Consider together how events in the story are linked: ask, **'Why did Jazz not let Ollie into the tent at first?'**, **'How did Jazz set up her puppet theatre?'**

Book knowledge

CLL 4 knowing about books and print; **NLS** T1

- Before you read the book, talk about the cover. Ask the child to show you the front cover, back cover and title. Find the title page and the author's name.

- When you read the book, use words like **'beginning'**, **'end'**, **'word'**, **'letter'**, **'capital letter'**.

Independent reading

CLL 4 reading independently; **NLS** T2, T3, T8

- Encourage the child to read the repeated parts of the book. Start by reading to the child pages 2 and 3, which introduce the first repeated phrase. On page 4, ask the child to take over, using the pictures to help work out difficult words (**'box'**, **'torch'**).

- Ask the child to point to the words as he or she reads them and ensure that he or she does so correctly. Pointing helps the child to focus on the words rather than just remembering phrases.

- Make sure the child does not read like a robot: encourage fluency.

- Help the child to read page 6. Remind the child of the title, or ask him or her to look at the picture and guess what Ollie is saying before reading the text.

- If the child is struggling, read the first few words on each page yourself, and prompt the child to join in with familiar phrases. Once the story is familiar, the child will be able to re-read it with confidence.

- Praise the child for 'having a go'.

First words

CLL 4 reading common words; **NLS** W5, W6

- When reading the story for the second or third time, draw attention to repeated words: for example, **'went'**, **'to'**, **'she'**, **'get'**, **'come'**, **'said'**. These are from the National Literacy Strategy's list of common ('high-frequency') words, taught in the Reception year. For a list of all the high-frequency words used in the story, please see the box on the inside back cover.

- Show the child one of the words listed above and ask him or her to find it on another page. Later, look for these words in other books and in signs and instructions that you see during the day.

- Talk about words starting with the same letter, such as **'can'** and **'come'** (pages 6 and 10). What is different about these two words?

- The word **'said'** is a difficult word, but children learn that it is used in stories whenever characters say something. Look through some stories and find what the characters **'said'**.

- Ensure that the child remains interested. If the child loses interest, stop.

Letters and letter sounds

CLL 3 linking sounds to letters; using phonic knowledge; **NLS** W2, W3

- Remind the child that the first letter of an unknown word, together with any clues in the picture, will help in working out what it is. For example (pages 6 and 10) **'"Can I come in?" s___ Ollie.'**

- Show the child a letter shape and say the sound. See how many times the child can find the letter. For example, **'t'** (in **'tent'**, **'went'**, **'to'**).

- Say the words **'she'** and **'show'**, exaggerating the **'sh'** sound. Explain that two letters together (**'s'** and **'h'**) make this **'sh'** sound. Point to the **'sh'** words in this book (**'she'** on pages 3, 4, 5 and 9; **'show'** on page 12).

- Show the child how to build simple three-letter words by saying the letter sounds and blending them (for example, **'b-o-x'** or **'g-e-t'**, page 4).

Language development

CLL 1 extending vocabulary; using spoken language;　**CLL 2** talking to organise ideas

- Link the story to the child's own experience of puppets, or encourage the child to think about making some: **'What could we use to make a puppet?'**, **'How would we make it?'** Encourage the child to explain and elaborate.

- Make puppets out of old socks, gloves or paper bags: use them to act out favourite stories.

- Use the story for talking about feelings. Discuss how Ollie might feel at different points: for example, when Jazz won't let him into the tent (page 7). Relate this to the child's own experience of feeling excluded.

Retelling the story

CLL 4 retelling narratives;　**NLS** T4, T7

- Encourage the child to describe the events in order, for example: **'How does the story start?'**, **'What happens next?'**

- Show the pictures on pages 2 and 3 and start the story in your own words. Include details omitted from the text: for example, **'One *sunny day* Jazz made a tent *out of* …'**, **'Ollie was busy …'** Encourage the child to take over, using the pictures in a similar way.

Note for schools and nurseries

Each set of activities outlined above relates to the area of learning described as 'Communication, Language and Literacy' (CLL), as set out in the document *Curriculum guidance for the Foundation Stage* (Qualifications and Curriculum Authority, 2000). The aspects of learning covered by **Daisy Lane Home–School Readers** are as follows:

CLL 1 Language for communication　　**CLL 3** Linking sounds and letters
CLL 2 Language for thinking　　**CLL 4** Reading

The symbol **NLS** indicates references to the National Literacy Strategy at text (T), sentence (S) and word (W) level – all of them taken from the objectives for children in Reception classes.

The Daisy Lane Reading Profile: Series A (ISBN 0 7217 1114 6), available separately, is a one-per-child record booklet designed to accompany the readers for young children. Use it to inform planning and to provide direct evidence of a child's reading skills. Contact Schofield & Sims for further details.